FIRST PUBLISHED IN GREAT BRITAIN 2014 BY
BEAST IN SHOW BOOKS
PO BOX 337, ILKLEY, WEST YORKSHIRE, LS29 1GN
WWW.BEASTINSHOW.COM

A CIP CATALOGUE RECORD FOR THIS TITLE IS AVAILABLE
FROM THE BRITISH LIBRARY

ISBN 978-0-9929067-0-2

PRINTED IN CHINA

THIS BOOK
BELONGS
TO:

-- -- -- -- -- -- -- -- -- --

FOR EVERYONE WHO HAS BELIEVED IN THIS BOOK.

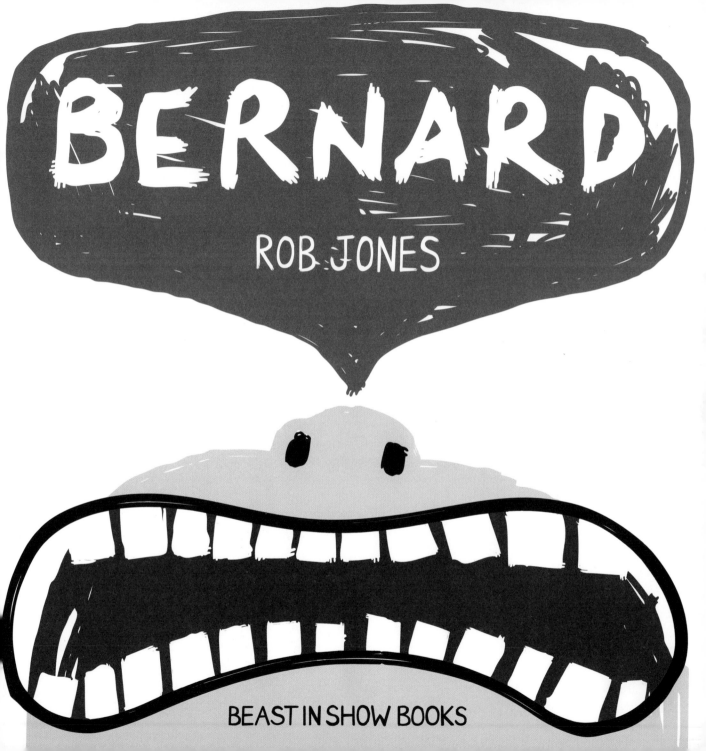

BERNARD

ROB JONES

BEAST IN SHOW BOOKS

AND ONE OF HIS PAWS WAS AS BIG AS YOUR HEAD!

BECAUSE THEY NEVER KNEW WHEN HE MIGHT COME ROUND

HE EVER
HE WOULD
UP HIS

NOUT

THIS BEAST'S NAME IS BERNARD AND HE WOULDN'T EVEN EAT

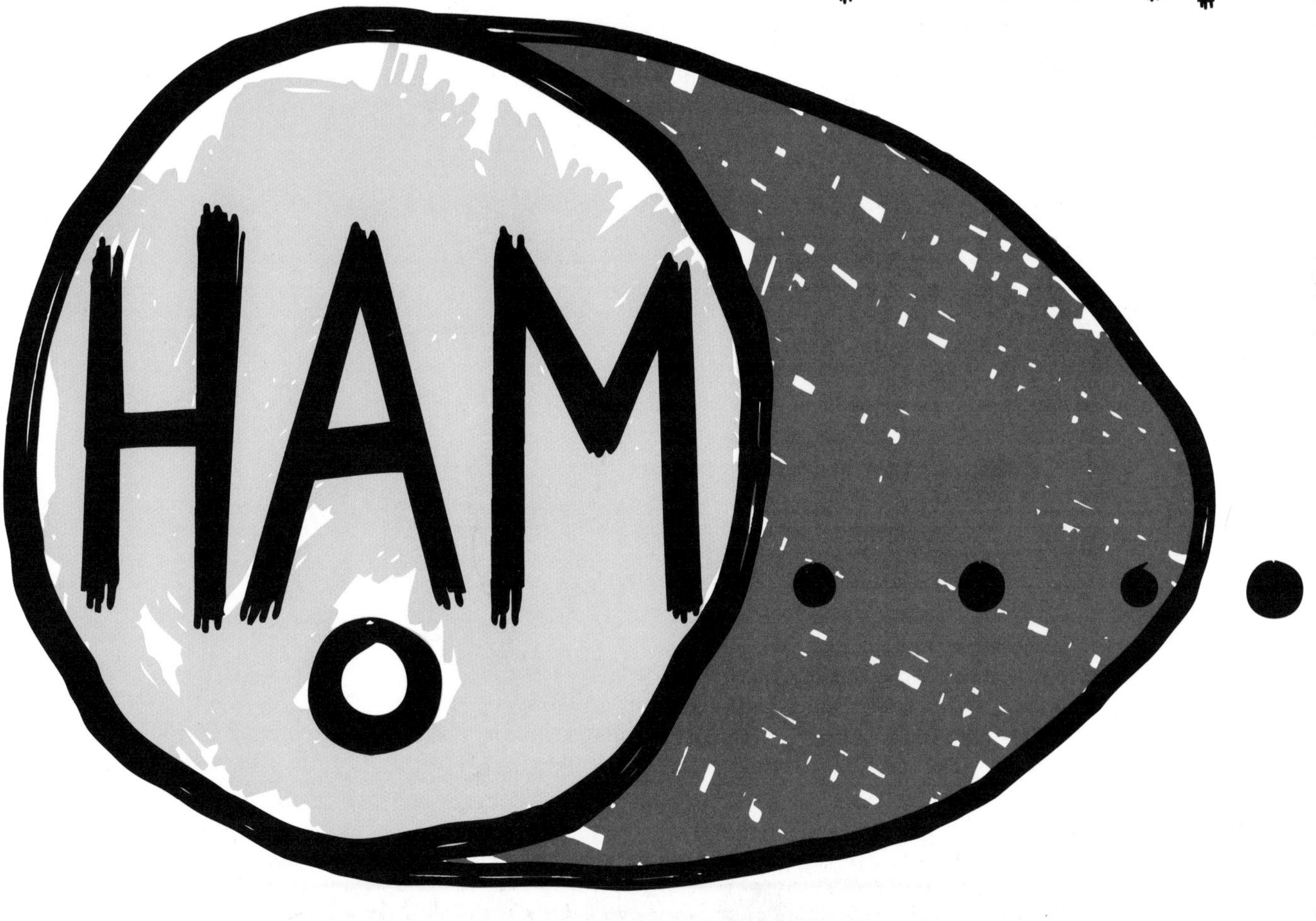

AND
BLOCK
UP YOUR
DOORS

BECAUSE IF YOU'VE

GOT JAM...

JAM

BEAST IN SHOW BOOKS IS A NEW
PUBLISHING VENTURE BROUGHT TO YOU BY
BEAST IN SHOW, A GIFT AND HOMEWARES
PRODUCTION COMPANY SPECIALISING IN
APPLIED GRAPHICS.

WWW.BEASTINSHOW.COM

ROB JONES IS AN ILLUSTRATOR BASED IN OXFORDSHIRE. HE RECEIVED A 1ST CLASS DEGREE IN ILLUSTRATION FROM THE UNIVERSITY OF GLOUCESTERSHIRE IN 2011 AND HAS BEEN CREATING CHILDREN'S BOOKS AND COLLECTABLE ART TOYS SINCE GRADUATING.

WWW.THEONEANDONLYJONES.CO.UK